FROM THE F

Harry Potter™

HOGWARTS JOURNAL

WELCOME TO HOGWARTS!

Imagine that you have received your Letter of Acceptance to Hogwarts School of Witchcraft and Wizardry! What wonder awaits at a school where anything can happen?

Record all your magical memories in the pages that follow, as well as your adventures and achievements from the Muggle world to complete a journal to treasure for centuries.

Introduce yourself here.

My first name(s):

DARCIE C-P

My surname:

CAOMORE - PHILLIPS

My birthday:

19/05/98

My nickname:

DARC

I am a:

- [✓] witch
- [ ] wizard
- [ ] Squib

SCHOOL SUPPLIES

Hogwarts students spend their Sickles, Knuts and Galleons on school supplies at Diagon Alley. Draw something you might buy at each shop.

Flourish and Blotts Bookshop

Quality Quidditch Supplies

SEPTEMBER

A wand is a witch or wizard's most important tool. No two wands are the same and the magical objects choose their owners. Ollivanders wand shop has been selling wands for centuries.

What sort of wand would be right for you? Think about its properties, then draw a wondrous wand below.

Wood:

☐ Holly   ☑ Vine   ☐ Elder   ☐ Willow   ☐ Yew

Core:

☐ Thestral tail hair   ☑ Dragon heartstring

☐ Phoenix feather   ☐ Unicorn tail hair

EXPRESS DELIVERY

All aboard the Hogwarts Express! Most students travel to the wizarding school on a train that leaves from Platform Nine and Three-Quarters at King's Cross Station in London.
Who would you want to share a carriage with on your journey to Hogwarts? Tick up to three companions.

HARRY POTTER   **RON WEASLEY**   **NEVILLE LONGBOTTOM**

HERMIONE GRANGER   **LUNA LOVEGOOD**   **LEE JORDAN**

DRACO MALFOY

LONDON TO HOGWARTS

PLATFORM 9 3/4

for ONE WAY travel

Imagine the Honeydukes trolley is heading your way. Which sweet treat would you most want to try?

☑ Chocolate Frogs   ☐ Jelly Slugs   ☐ Liquorice Wands

☐ Cauldron Cakes   ☑ Pumpkin Pasties

Draw your choice here.

THE SORTING HAT

The ancient Sorting Hat has been at Hogwarts longer than Albus Dumbledore himself! It decides which of the four famous houses students should be placed into — Gryffindor, Hufflepuff, Ravenclaw or Slytherin.

GRYFFINDOR
FOUNDER: Godric Gryffindor
ARTEFACT: the shining Sword of Gryffindor
HEAD OF HOUSE: Professor McGonagall
QUALITIES OF GRYFFINDORS: courageous, brave and determined
FAMOUS GRYFFINDORS: Harry Potter, the Weasley Family, Hermione Granger, Neville Longbottom

SLYTHERIN
FOUNDER: Salazar Slytherin
ARTEFACT: a locket adorned with a glittering serpent
HEAD OF HOUSE: Professor Snape
QUALITIES OF SLYTHERINS: proud, cunning and ambitious
FAMOUS SLYTHERINS: Draco Malfoy, Tom Riddle, Bellatrix Lestrange

HUFFLEPUFF

FOUNDER: Helga Hufflepuff
ARTEFACT: a golden cup
HEAD OF HOUSE: Professor Sprout
QUALITIES OF HUFFLEPUFFS:
patient, hardworking, loyal and fair
FAMOUS HUFFLEPUFFS:
Newt Scamander, Cedric Diggory,
Nymphadora Tonks

RAVENCLAW

FOUNDER: Rowena Ravenclaw
ARTEFACT: the Lost Diadem of Ravenclaw
HEAD OF HOUSE: Professor Flitwick
QUALITIES OF RAVENCLAWS:
wise, eager to learn and quick-witted
FAMOUS RAVENCLAWS:
Luna Lovegood, Cho Chang, Professor Trelawney

In which house do you think the
Sorting Hat would place you?

HUFFLEPUFF

DREAM DORM

You'll always find a home at Hogwarts! The dormitories are cosy and a friendly face is never far away. Which Muggle comforts would you bring to school with you? Draw some items you'd definitely pack in your trunk.

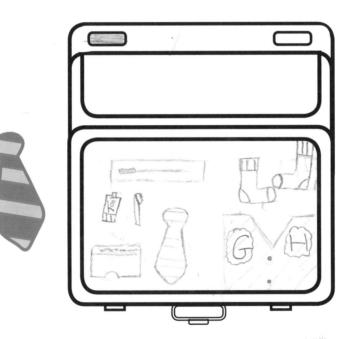

What would be the password to your dormitory?

19207

Think of two people you'd like to share your dorm with.

Name: Nymphadora Tonks

Why: _____

_____

Portrait:

Name: Susan Bones

Why: _____

_____

Portrait:

TERM TIMETABLE

Hogwarts School of Witchcraft and Wizardry is one of the finest wizarding schools in the world. It has a class to suit every young witch or wizard, whatever their talent.

Here are just some of the spellbinding subjects taught at Hogwarts. Circle each one you'd like to study.

Potions   Charms   Defence Against the Dark Arts

Transfiguration   Herbology

Care of Magical Creatures   Flying Lessons

Muggle Studies   Divination

What do you think your favourite subject might be?

Fill in this lesson planner to timetable your subjects at Hogwarts or use it for your studies in the Muggle world. Don't forget to include what you do when the school day ends — is Quidditch practice or homework in the library your preference?

	MONDAY	TUESDAY	WEDNESDAY	THURSDAY	FRIDAY
MORNING	FLying Lesson				
AFTERNOON					
AFTER-SCHOOL ACTIVITIES					

MY SEPTEMBER MEMORIES

Record your favourite memories from your first month at Hogwarts or describe your adventures in the Muggle world.

Week 1

_____

_____

_____

_____

Week 2

_____

_____

_____

_____

Week 3

_____

_____

_____

_____

Week 4

_____

_____

_____

_____

HALLOWE'EN AT HOGWARTS

From troll invasions to the opening of the Chamber of Secrets, October at Hogwarts is often an eventful month! On the last day of the month, Hallowe'en is celebrated, with an enormous feast in the Great Hall.

Tick the Hallowe'en treats you'd dare to try:

Food

☑ **Pumpkin Pasties**   ☐ **Treacle Tart**

☑ **Fudge Flies**   ☑ **Fizzing Whizzbees**

☐ **Cauldron Cakes**   ☐ **Hagrid's Rock Cakes**

Drinks

☑ **Pumpkin Juice**   ☑ **Butterbeer**

☐ **Nettle Wine**

OCTOBER

Now decide on how to decorate the Great Hall:

Decorations

☑ floating pumpkin lanterns ☐ fake bats

☐ candles ☑ spider webs

LUMINOUS LANTERNS

The pumpkins in Hagrid's pumpkin patch grow to an extraordinary size! Colour in one of Hagrid's pumpkins, ready to celebrate Hallowe'en.

Trick or Treat?

How will you celebrate Hallowe'en in the Muggle world?
Plan a spooky night below.

What will your costume be?

_____

What is your favourite trick to play?

_____

Who might you play it on?

SEREN
_____

What is your favourite treat?

_____

CREATURE COMPANIONS

First-year pupils at Hogwarts are allowed an animal companion. Match Harry's friends to their pets.

A

HARRY POTTER

D

RON WEASLEY

B

HERMIONE GRANGER

C

NEVILLE LONGBOTTOM

A

HEDWIG

B

CROOKSHANKS

C

TREVOR

D

SCABBERS

If you could choose a pet, real or magical, what would it be?
Draw your ideal animal in the space below.

MY OCTOBER MEMORIES

Record your Hogwarts highlights for October
or describe your adventures in the Muggle world.

Week 1

_____

_____

_____

_____

Week 2

_____

_____

_____

_____

Week 3

Week 4

SPELLBINDING SPORT

The month of November marks the start of the Quidditch season at Hogwarts. The wizarding sport is played on broomsticks at lightning pace!

It's time for Quidditch trials. Which position would best suit you?

- [ ] **KEEPER** - the Keeper's job is to guard the three goal hoops and prevent the opposition from scoring. Must be athletic and agile.

- [ ] **BEATER** - Beaters bat away the dangerous Bludgers from hitting their own team into the direction of the opposition. Must be fearless.

- [x] **CHASER** - the Chasers control the Quaffle and try to get it through the hoops to score. Must be fast and creative flyers.

- [ ] **SEEKER** - it's up to the Seeker to catch the Golden Snitch and claim victory for their team. Must be lightning-fast and expert broomstick handlers.

Design a new kit for your Hogwarts house team,
including a brand-new broom.

TRIWIZARD TOURNAMENT

In Harry's fourth year, he was an unwilling contestant in the Triwizard Tournament, a famous contest between the wizarding schools of Hogwarts, Durmstrang and Beauxbatons. Decide how difficult you might find each of these tasks.

1. Stealing a golden dragon egg:

[✓] tricky [ ] confounding [✓] almost certainly impossible

2. Rescuing a friend from the Great Lake:

[ ] tricky [✓] confounding [ ] almost certainly impossible

3. Completing a maze to find the Triwizard Cup:

[ ] tricky [ ] confounding [✓] almost certainly impossible

Imagine there was a fourth challenge, what might it be?
Pruning the Whomping Willow? Riding a Kelpie?
Draw it or write about it below.

MY NOVEMBER MEMORIES

Record your favourite memories from November at Hogwarts
or write about your month in the Muggle world.

Week 1

Week 2

Week 3

_____

_____

_____

_____

Week 4

_____

_____

_____

_____

THE YULE BALL

Harry and his friends attended the Yule Ball on Christmas Day during Harry's fourth year at Hogwarts. Imagine you were joining in the yuletide fun!

Who would be your dream dance partner?

- [ ] Harry Potter
- [ ] Ron Weasley
- [ ] Hermione Granger
- [ ] Fleur Delacour
- [x] Viktor Krum
- [x] Cedric Diggory
- [ ] Ginny Weasley
- [ ] Neville Longbottom
- [ ] Luna Lovegood
- [ ] Cho Chang

Which type of music would you most like to dance to?

- [ ] a whirling waltz
- [ ] the Weird Sisters

What will you be wearing?

☐ old-fashioned dress robes like Ron

☑ a pretty gown like Hermione

☐ smart dress robes like Harry

Design your own winter outfit, complete with enchanting accessories.

ENCHANTED GIFTS

December is a month for the giving of gifts. Dumbledore gives
Harry the Potter family's rare and special Invisibility Cloak.
If you had a magical cloak, when would you wear it?
Imagine the scene here.

What gifts would you choose for others at Hogwarts?

Hermione Granger: A Necklace

Ron Weasley: _____

Harry Potter: _____

Dobby the House-Elf: _____

Luna Lovegood: _____

Neville Longbottom: _____

Now write a list of gift ideas for your own best friends:

_____

_____

_____

MY DECEMBER MEMORIES

Here you can write about this month's festive celebrations at Hogwarts or memories from the Muggle world.

Week 1

_____

_____

_____

_____

Week 2

_____

_____

_____

_____

Week 3

_____

_____

_____

_____

Week 4

_____

_____

_____

_____

TURNING TIME

With the Time-Turner, a magical object that allows time travel, Dumbledore gave Hermione the gift of time. Hermione and Harry used the Time-Turner to travel a few hours into the past and save Hagrid's Hippogriff, Buckbeak.

MAGICAL CREATURE

SPECIES: Hippogriff

FEATURES: horse-like creature with front legs, wings and head of an eagle.

HABITAT: temperate regions or forests

Imagine you have been given a Time-Turner,
where would you travel and why?

SEND A HOWLER

If you've never received a Howler, you are in luck!
These deafening letters explode if not opened quickly enough
and burn completely once the message has been read.

Think about a time you've done something forbidden
and write about it here. If you're as well-behaved
as Hermione, make something up!

_____

_____

_____

Who might send you a Howler for your misjudged deed?
A parent or grandparent or a teacher, perhaps?

_____

Now use this space to write the Howler
or send one to someone you know instead.

MY JANUARY MEMORIES

Which of January's events were the most memorable? Imagine your adventures at Hogwarts or write down some wondrous moments from the Muggle world.

Week 1

_____

_____

_____

_____

Week 2

_____

_____

_____

_____

Week 3

_____

_____

_____

_____

Week 4

_____

_____

_____

_____

ANIMAGI MAGIC

Animagi are witches and wizards who can transform into animals. The animal cannot be chosen, although it reflects a person's character. If you were an Animagus, what animal do you think you might be?

- ☐ cat
- ☐ rat
- ☐ unicorn
- ☑ dragon
- ☐ dog
- ☐ snake

Draw yourself in charming creature form here.

HOGWARTS LIBRARY

The Hogwarts Library stocks almost every magical book a witch or wizard could ever want to read. Beware though, some books at Hogwarts need to be handled with care!

Keep a record of the number of books you read over a whole year here. Are you a bookworm like Hermione or a reluctant reader like Ron?

- ☐ under 10 books
- ☐ 1-10 books
- ☑ 11-20 books
- ☐ 20-30 books
- ☐ more than 30 books

What is your favourite book and why?

_____

_____

_____

Design a cover for your very own book.

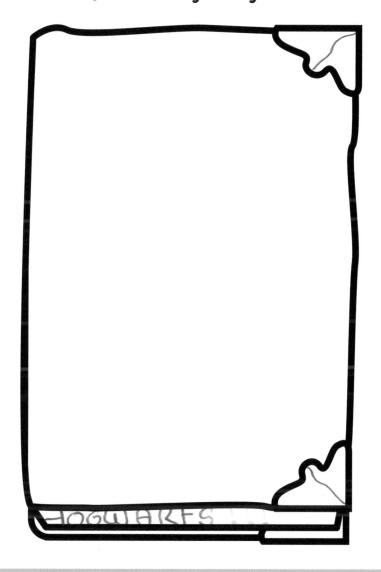

MY FEBRUARY MEMORIES

Which memories are your favourite from February? Describe them here or write down your best Muggle moments.

Week 1

_____

_____

_____

_____

Week 2

_____

_____

_____

_____

Week 3

_____

_____

_____

_____

Week 4

_____

_____

_____

_____

POWERFUL POTIONS

Let's see whether you have been paying attention in Potions class! Can you remember the purpose of each potion below?

Ageing Potion: _____

Amortentia: _____

Elixir of Life: _____

Felix Felicis: _____

Polyjuice Potion: _____

Veritaserum: _____

Colour in the deadly Mandrake Root to match its description.

IMPORTANT INGREDIENT

SPECIES: Mandrake Root

FEATURES: green leaves, brown roots,
a face not unlike a baby. Has a screech that can
be fatal to anyone within earshot

USAGE: a restorative draught to cure Petrification

DEFENCE AGAINST THE DARK ARTS

All students at Hogwarts must study Defence Against the Dark Arts to protect themselves against Dark magic. These professors have all taught the subject at Hogwarts. Number them in the order you'd like them to teach you — from the noble to the nasty.

2	Severus Snape	
5	Quirinus Quirrell	
3	Remus Lupin	
4	Dolores Umbridge	
1	Albus Dumbledore	

Harry defeated the most powerful Dark wizard at the Battle of Hogwarts. Finish doodling this Dark Mark, the symbol of You-Know-Who and his army of Death Eaters, to make it funny instead of scary.

MY MARCH MEMORIES

Here's the place to record March's most memorable moments from your weeks at Hogwarts or beyond.

Week 1

_____

_____

_____

_____

Week 2

_____

_____

_____

_____

Week 3

_____

_____

_____

_____

Week 4

_____

_____

_____

_____

APRIL FOOLS

Twins Fred and George Weasley are the biggest jokers in Hogwarts' history! Their inventions and jokes are perfect for April Fool's Day, which also happens to be their birthday. Which would you most like to test out?

- [x] switching identity with your identical twin

- [ ] taking an Ageing Potion

- [ ] offering someone a Canary Cream to turn them into a feathered bird

- [ ] setting off an entire box of Weasley's Wildfire Whizz-Bangs exploding fireworks

- [ ] exploding a foul-smelling Dungbomb at school

Draw your preferred joke in action here.

BEASTLY BOGGARTS

Boggarts are creatures that can appear in many different forms, depending on the witch or wizard's worst fear. *'Riddikulus!'* will cause the Boggart to change forms into something much funnier before it disappears.

Draw eight rollerskates on this giant Acromantula to help Ron banish his Boggart.

What might your Boggart be? Think of something that you find scary and draw it in its funniest form.

Practise saying 'RIDDIKULUS!' out loud.

MY APRIL MEMORIES

What wizarding memories did you make this month?
Write about all of April's adventures here.

Week 1

_____

_____

_____

_____

Week 2

_____

_____

_____

_____

Week 3

_____

_____

_____

_____

Week 4

_____

_____

_____

_____

SPELLS AND CHARMS

With a swish and flick of the wand and the all-important magical words, pupils must learn and practise many spells at Hogwarts if they are to become talented witches and wizards. Here are some of the simpler spells that are taught.

EXPELLIARMUS!	Removes an object (such as a wand) from an opponent's grip.
ACCIO!	Allows the witch or wizard to summon an object.
STUPEFY!	Stuns the enemy during a duel.
LUMOS!	Turns a wand into a torch to illuminate the area.
WINGARDIUM LEVIOSA!	A charm that can make things float.

MAY

Create your own spells below and write what each one does!

Spell: _____

Purpose: _____

_____

Spell: _____

Purpose: _____

_____

Spell: _____

Purpose: _____

_____

_____

EXPECTO PATRONUM

The powerful Patronus Charm is a defensive charm that is difficult to perform. The witch or wizard conjures an animal that protects them against dark creatures, such as Dementors.

Doodle patterns and add colour to these Dementors to make them look more friendly and less fearsome.

DUMBLEDORE'S ARMY

The Room of Requirement served as a meeting place for Dumbledore's Army — a secret society led by Harry that met to learn Defence Against the Dark Arts. Draw yourself and a friend as the missing members.

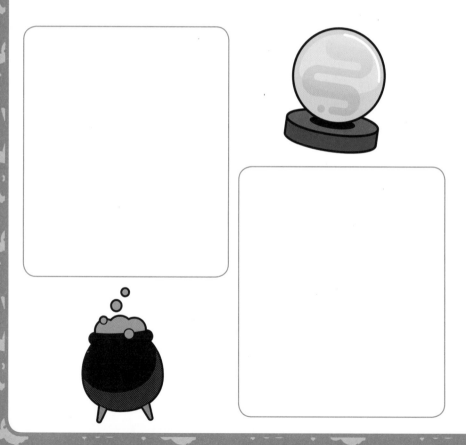

Write a signature for each of the four students who served as a leader of Dumbledore's Army, then solemnly swear you are up to no good!

Luna Lovegood

_____

H. Potter

_____

MY MAY MEMORIES

May is a month to make magical memories! Record some spellbinding souvenirs from this month below.

Week 1

_____

_____

_____

_____

Week 2

_____

_____

_____

_____

Week 3

_____

_____

_____

_____

Week 4

_____

_____

_____

_____

POLYJUICE POTION

Drinking a draught of Polyjuice Potion allows the drinker to appear as someone else. Brewing this potent potion isn't easy, though, and its effects can wear off at any moment.

Who would you like to temporarily transform into and why?

_____

_____

_____

_____

JUNE

70

Imagine you were brewing a powerful potion of your own.
What would it do? What might it be called?

Name: _____

Purpose: _____

Label your potion and colour it in.

CARE OF MAGICAL CREATURES

The Forbidden Forest is home to some fantastic beasts.
Many magical creatures from Pixies to unicorns to dragons live
there. Pupils can learn Care of Magical Creatures in
their third year at Hogwarts.

Thestrals are flying horse-like creatures that are invisible except to those who have seen death. Colour in the ghostly Thestral to bring it to life.

MY JUNE MEMORIES

How was the month of June for you? Write down the events from this month using ancient runes (or just in English).

Week 1

Week 2

Week 3

_____

_____

_____

_____

Week 4

_____

_____

_____

_____

BIRTHDAY BOY

When Hagrid bakes a cake for Harry's eleventh birthday, it's the first birthday cake the boy wizard has ever had! Imagine you are making a cake for Harry's next birthday, what will it look like?

Sponge:

☑ chocolate ☐ carrot ☐ pumpkin ☐ rainbow

Icing:

☐ chocolate ☐ lemon ☑ strawberry

Decorations:

☑ sprinkles ☐ Chocolate Frogs

☑ Bertie Bott's Every Flavour Beans

☑ candles ☐ sparklers

Now decorate the cake for a delicious-looking treat.

GRINGOTTS GUARDS

Gringotts Bank is the wizarding world's most secure bank.
Gold-loving goblins and dangerous dragons guard the treasure
of witches and wizards in special underground vaults.
Doodle some scales on this grizzly guard.

Imagine you were visiting your own Gringotts vault,
what treasures might be inside? Draw some gold,
a secret scroll or another prized possession.

MY JULY MEMORIES

School's out in the month of July!
What were some of your holiday highlights this month?

Week 1

_____

_____

_____

_____

Week 2

_____

_____

_____

_____

Week 3

_____

_____

_____

_____

Week 4

_____

_____

_____

_____

AUGUST ADVENTURES

August is the only month when Hogwarts castle is closed to pupils. What adventures beckon beyond the castle grounds? A special event or a visit to faraway friends, perhaps? Draw your dream destination, and then fill in the lists on the next page.

Three things I would do:

1. _____

2. _____

3. _____

Three things I would take with me:

1. _____

2. _____

3. _____

HERMIONE'S HANDBAG

When Harry, Ron and Hermione were hunting Horcruxes, Hermione's magically expanding handbag transported everything the friends needed, from cooking equipment to tents! What would you pack for your travels?

Missing Hogwarts? Write postcards to your friends to keep in touch, and then send them by Owl Post.

™ & © WBEI. (s19)

™ & © WBEI. (s19)

Harry Potter

MY AUGUST MEMORIES

Record your favourite summer holiday memories from August or write about your adventures in the Muggle world.

Week 1

_____

_____

_____

_____

Week 2

_____

_____

_____

_____

Week 3

_____

_____

_____

_____

Week 4

_____

_____

_____

_____

A YEAR OF MAGICAL MEMORIES

What a magical year! Write down some special memories that will last a lifetime, even after drinking the Elixir of Life!

The best thing that happened to me was:

_____

_____

_____

Some new friends I made were:

_____

_____

I felt most proud when:

_____

_____

Use this space to draw or stick in a photo of
your most magical memory of the year.

PREDICTING THE FUTURE

Imagine you are back in Professor Trelawney's Divination class.
Look into your crystal ball. What do you see in your future?
Draw your vision below.